Don't be a Goop!

by Frank Gelett Burgess

TOP THAT

Licensed exclusively to Top That Publishing Ltd
Tide Mill Way, Woodbridge, Suffolk, IP12 1AP, UK
www.topthatpublishing.com
Copyright © 2013 Tide Mill Media
All rights reserved
2 4 6 8 9 7 5 3 1
Manufactured in China

Illustrated by Maxine Lee
Written by Frank Gelett Burgess

ISBN 978-1-78244-225-7

A catalogue record for this book is available from the British Library

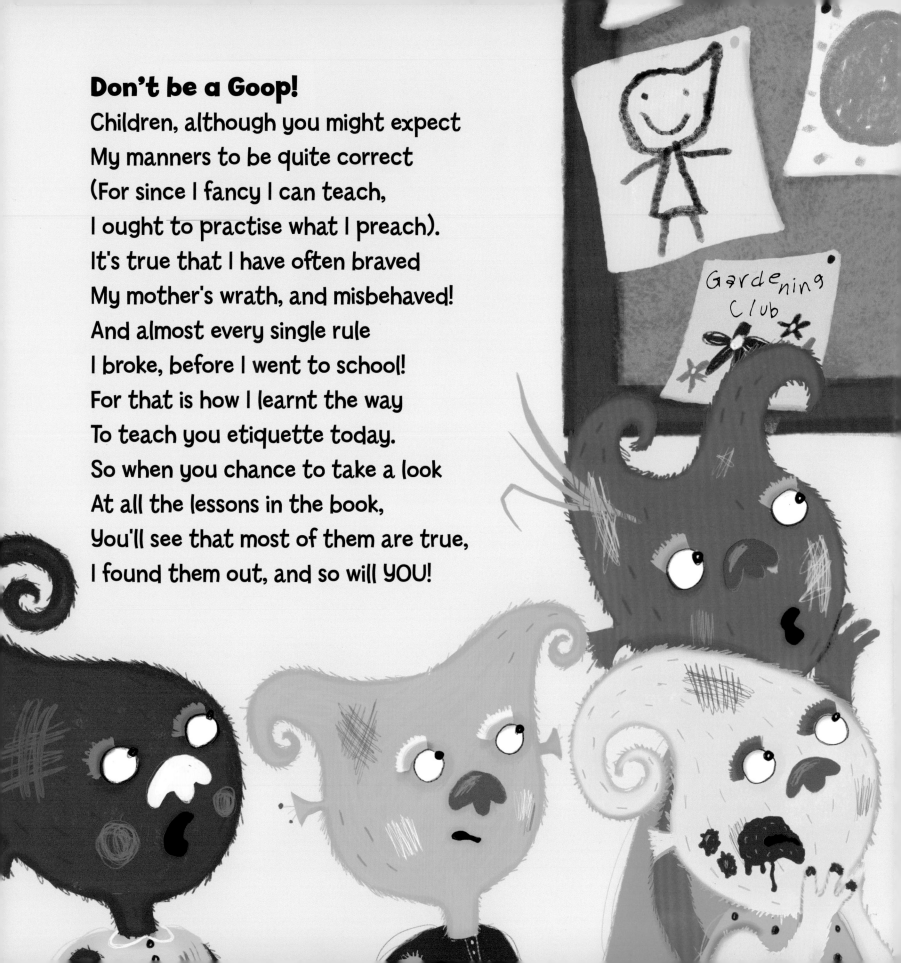

Don't be a Goop!

Children, although you might expect
My manners to be quite correct
(For since I fancy I can teach,
I ought to practise what I preach).
It's true that I have often braved
My mother's wrath, and misbehaved!
And almost every single rule
I broke, before I went to school!
For that is how I learnt the way
To teach you etiquette today.
So when you chance to take a look
At all the lessons in the book,
You'll see that most of them are true,
I found them out, and so will YOU!

Gardening
Club

Lesson 1
Candy in the cushions
Of the easy chair;
Raisins in the sofa –
How did they get there?

The little Goop who's greedy
Does it every day,
Like a little puppy,
Hiding bones away!

Lesson 2

Do you slam the door?

Do you drag your feet?

Making noise enough for four

Hundred thousand Goops, or more,

Tearing up the street.

Clattering down the stairs,
Storming through the hall,
Pounding floors, upsetting chairs.
Do you think anyone cares
For your noise, at all?

Lesson 3

There once was a Goop (it is hard to believe
Such unpleasant behaviour of you!)
Who was always wiping his nose on his sleeve;
I hope that this Goop wasn't you!

He was always spitting (for fun, I suppose),
I couldn't believe it of you!
And putting his fingers up into his nose;
I KNOW that this Goop wasn't YOU!

Lesson 4

Why is it Goops must always wish
To touch each apple in the dish?
Why do they never neatly fold
Their napkins until they are told?

Why do they play with food, and bite
Such awful mouthfuls? Is it right?
Why do they tilt back in their chairs?
Because they're Goops! So no one cares!

Lesson 5

Goop! Goop! Goop!
I wish you'd wash your face!
Goop! Goop! Goop!
Your hands are a disgrace!
Goop! Goop! Goop!
Put things back in their place!
I wish you were polite,
Instead of a
Goop! Goop! Goop!

Lesson 6

Don't try to tell a story
To beat the one you've heard;
For if you try, you're bound to lie,
And that would be absurd!

Don't try to be more funny
Than anyone in school;
For if you're not, they'll laugh a lot,
And think you are a fool!

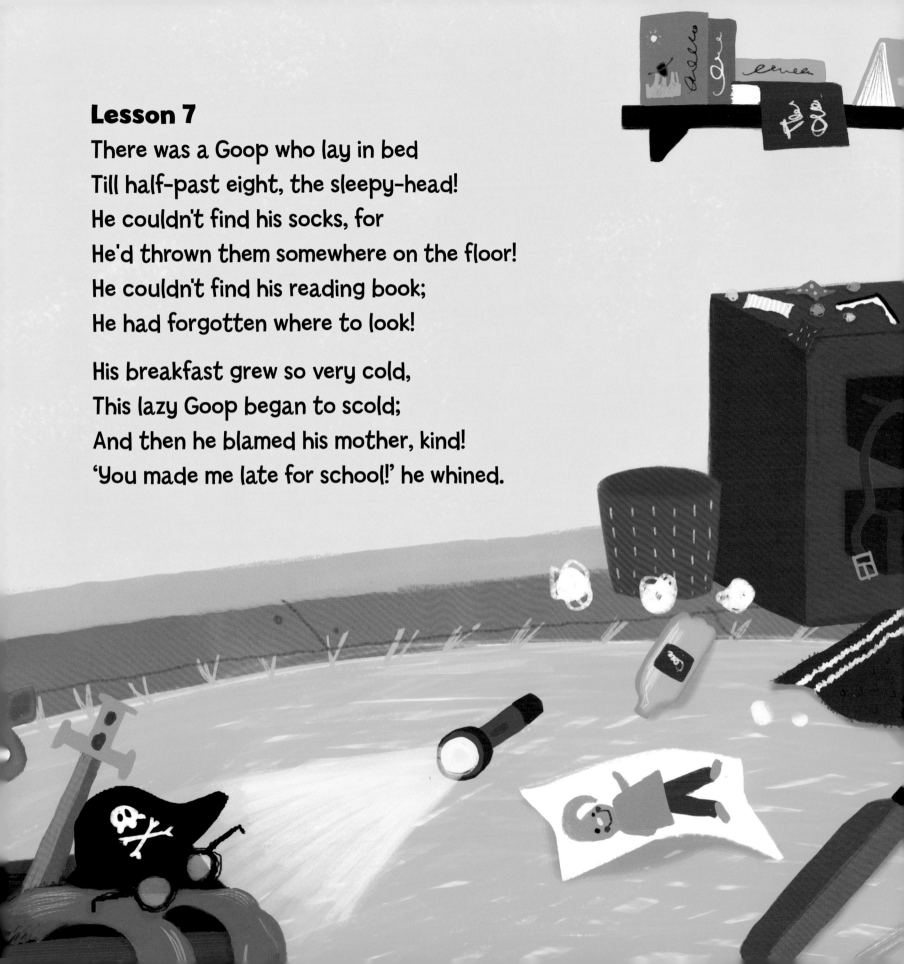

Lesson 7

There was a Goop who lay in bed
Till half-past eight, the sleepy-head!
He couldn't find his socks, for
He'd thrown them somewhere on the floor!
He couldn't find his reading book;
He had forgotten where to look!

His breakfast grew so very cold,
This lazy Goop began to scold;
And then he blamed his mother, kind!
'You made me late for school!' he whined.

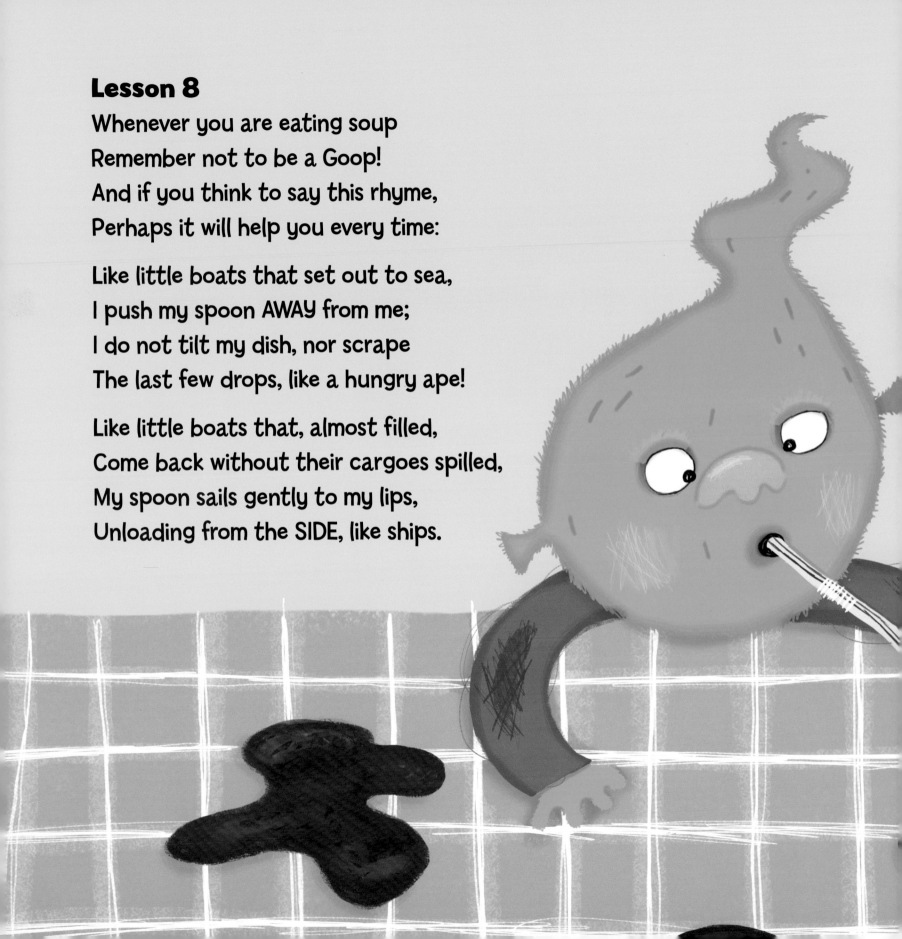

Lesson 8

Whenever you are eating soup
Remember not to be a Goop!
And if you think to say this rhyme,
Perhaps it will help you every time:

Like little boats that set out to sea,
I push my spoon AWAY from me;
I do not tilt my dish, nor scrape
The last few drops, like a hungry ape!

Like little boats that, almost filled,
Come back without their cargoes spilled,
My spoon sails gently to my lips,
Unloading from the SIDE, like ships.

When you are fetching bread, I trust
You never nibble at the crust.

When in the kitchen, do you linger,
And pinch the cookies with your finger?

Or do you peck the frosted cake?
Don't do it, please, for goodness sake!

Lesson 10

There are about a thousand things
I'm not allowed to do;
Most everything I'm fondest of
I'm told is wrong – are you?

They say, 'Please don't do that, my child!'
They say, 'You mustn't, dear!'
I hope sometime I'll learn what's right,
For now, I've no idea!